Book 1 Age 7-8

TABLE TEASERS

Peter Patilla, David Godber, Alan Brighouse

MACMILLAN
EDUCATION

Patilla. Peter
  Table teasers.
  Bk. 1 : 7-9 years
  1. Arithmetic – Examinations. questions. etc.
  I. Title II. Godber. David III. Brighouse.
  Alan
  513'.2'076   QA115
  ISBN 0-333-43954-6

First published 1987

Published by
MACMILLAN EDUCATION LTD
Houndmills, Basingstoke, Hampshire RG21 2XS
and London
Companies and representatives
throughout the world

Illustrated by Michael Evans

Designed by the Pen & Ink Book Company Ltd

Produced by AMR for Macmillan Education Ltd

EGG TIME

Work out the table fact on each egg cup.
Draw the eggs in the right egg cups.

2 × 1 = 2
2 × 2 = 4
2 × 3 = 6
2 × 4 = 8
2 × 5 = 10
2 × 6 = 12
2 × 7 = 14
2 × 8 = 16
2 × 9 = 18
2 × 10 = 20

6   10   2   14   20

16   4   8   12   18

8
2 × 4

12
2 × 6

14
2 × 7

6
2 × 3

18
2 × 9

2
2 × 1

20
2 × 10

16
2 × 8

10
2 × 5

4
2 × 2

3

COLOUR MATCH

Work out the table facts in this table.
Use the colour code for the picture.

2 × 1 Red	2 × 5 Dark Blue	2 × 2 Green	2 × 4 Yellow	2 × 3 Purple
2 × 9 Brown	2 × 7 Orange	2 × 10 Black	2 × 8 Pink	2 × 6 Light Blue

4

KNIVES AND FORKS

Work out the table fact on each fork.
Join each fork to its knife.

$3 \times 1 = $ 3
$3 \times 2 = $ 6
$3 \times 3 = $ 9
$3 \times 4 = $ 12
$3 \times 5 = $ 15
$3 \times 6 = $ 18
$3 \times 7 = $ 21
$3 \times 8 = $ 24
$3 \times 9 = $ 27
$3 \times 10 = $ 30

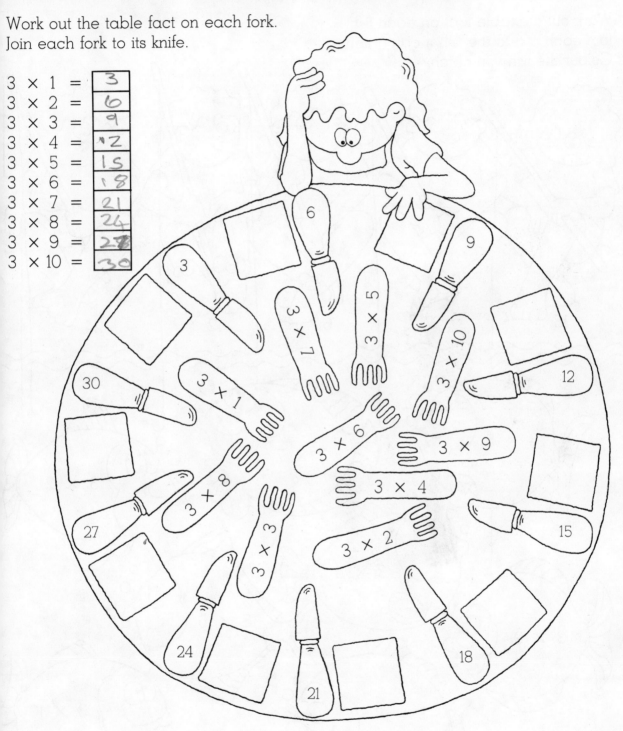

GONE FISHING

Work out the table fact on each fish.
Join each rod to the fish it can catch.
Colour the fish you catch.

18   27   6   12   24

3 × 5   3 × 7   3 × 2   3 × 4   3 × 6   3 × 9   3 × 8   3 × 10

6

SEWING TIME

Work out the table facts.
Join each button to its needle and thread.

4 × 1 = 4
4 × 2 = 8
4 × 3 = 12
4 × 4 = 16
4 × 5 = 20
4 × 6 = 24
4 × 7 = 28
4 × 8 = 32
4 × 9 = 36
4 × 10 = 40

TABLE WHEEL

Find each answer of your 4 × table in order (e.g. 4 × 1=4).
Write the first letter of each picture as you come to it.
You will find the names of two birds.
What are they?

SHAKERS AND DICE

Work out the table facts on each shaker.
Join each dice to its shaker.

5 × 1 =	5	
5 × 2 =	10	
5 × 3 =	15	
5 × 4 =	20	
5 × 5 =	25	
5 × 6 =	30	
5 × 7 =	35	
5 × 8 =	40	
5 × 9 =	45	
5 × 10 =	50	

25   45   5

20   10   35

50

15   40   30

5 × 7   5 × 6   5 × 10

5 × 1

5 × 9   5 × 8

5 × 4   5 × 3   5 × 2   5 × 5

9

DOT-TO-DOT

Join the dots and see what appears.
Begin at 5 and count on in 5s.

TABLE BEETLES

Work out the table facts.
Join each beetle to its stone.

$6 \times 1 = $ 6
$6 \times 2 = $ 12
$6 \times 3 = $ 18
$6 \times 4 = $ 24
$6 \times 5 = $ 30
$6 \times 6 = $ 36
$6 \times 7 = $ 42
$6 \times 8 = $ 48
$6 \times 9 = $ 54
$6 \times 10 = $ 60

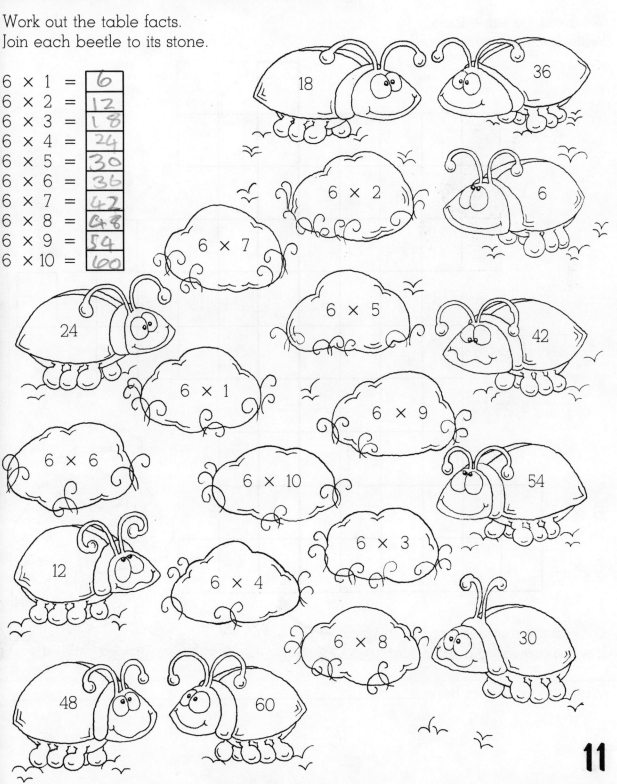

TABLE WORDS

Work out the table facts.
Write each answer in words.

6 × 1 | S | I | X

6 × 3

6 × 2

6 × 8

6 × 4

6 × 6

6 × 10

6 × 5

6 × 7

6 × 9

Look at the number word in this box.
It is the answer to a table fact.

Write the table fact here: _____

TABLE ROCKETS

Work out the table facts.
Join each rocket to its star.

7 × 1 = 7
7 × 2 = 14
7 × 3 =
7 × 4 =
7 × 5 = 35
7 × 6 =
7 × 7 =
7 × 8 =
7 × 9 =
7 × 10 = 70

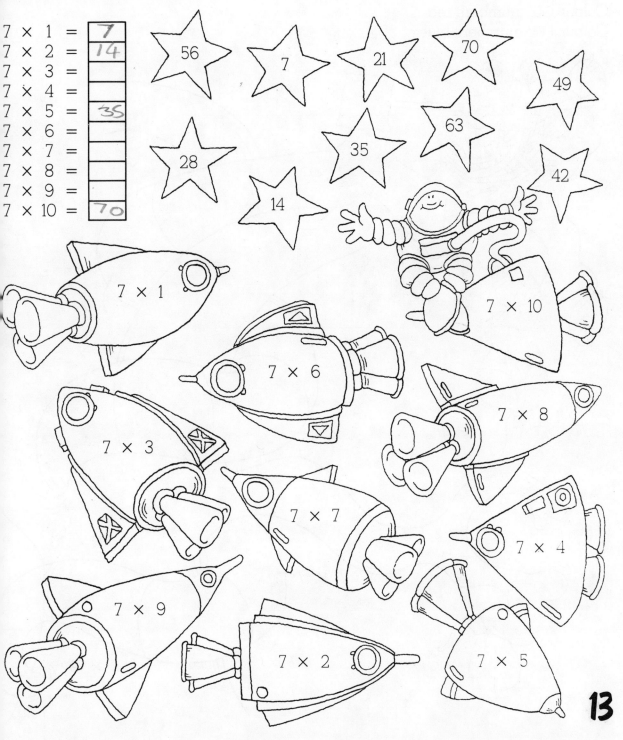

A SLITHERY PROBLEM

Work out the table facts.
Write the answers on the snake.
Colour ODD numbers red.
Colour EVEN numbers blue.

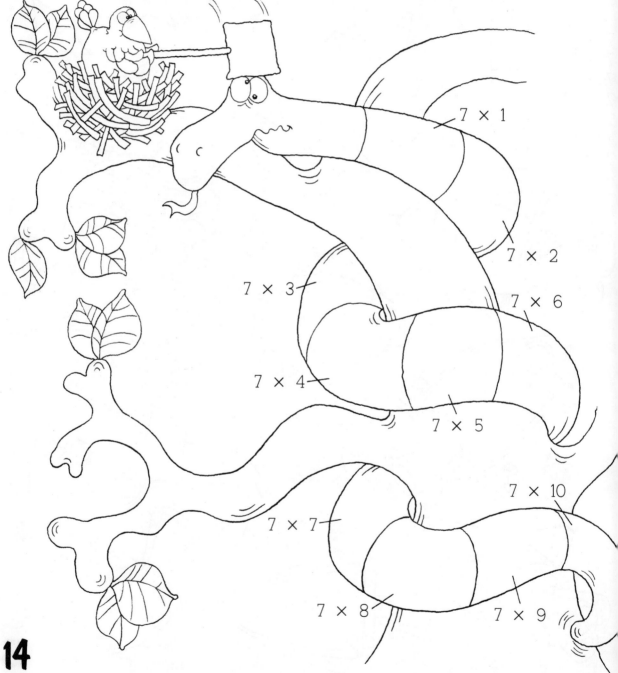

7×1

7×2

7×3

7×6

7×4

7×5

7×10

7×7

7×8

7×9

14

TIE THEM UP

Work out the table facts.
Draw a line from each octopus to its boat.

$8 \times 1 =$ 8
$8 \times 2 =$ 18
$8 \times 3 =$
$8 \times 4 =$
$8 \times 5 =$ 40
$8 \times 6 =$
$8 \times 7 =$
$8 \times 8 =$
$8 \times 9 =$
$8 \times 10 =$ 80

15

BURYING BONES

The dogs can bury bones that belong to the 8 × table.
Colour the bones they can bury.

TABLE LADYBIRDS

Work out the table facts.
Join each ladybird to its leaf.

9 × 1 =	9	
9 × 2 =	18	
9 × 3 =	27	
9 × 4 =	36	
9 × 5 =	65	
9 × 6 =	54	
9 × 7 =	63	
9 × 8 =	72	
9 × 9 =	81	
9 × 10 =	90	

WORD SEARCHER

Find words that belong to the 9 × table.
One word has been done for you.

S	E	I	G	H	T	Y	O	N	E	V
I	A	C	B	O	W	V	M	I	A	G
X	G	H	K	L	E	S	N	N	D	F
T	P	D	X	S	N	D	G	E	I	O
Y	T	F	I	F	T	Y	F	O	U	R
T	H	I	R	T	Y	S	I	X	O	T
H	A	Y	S	G	S	A	H	V	S	Y
R	D	B	I	X	E	C	N	T	E	F
E	F	O	U	T	V	.P	I	M	D	I
E	I	G	H	T	E	E	N	A	C	V
P	V	N	I	N	N	R	E	K	V	E
S	E	V	E	N	T	Y	T	W	O	X
A	C	V	M	B	O	K	Y	H	B	S

18

TEA-TIME

Work out the table facts.
Draw a line from each cake to its plate.

10 × 1 = 10
10 × 2 = 20
10 × 3 = 30
10 × 4 = 40
10 × 5 = 50
10 × 6 = 60
10 × 7 = 70
10 × 8 = 80
10 × 9 = 90
10 × 10 = 100

FLYING HIGH

Look at the numbers on the children.
Follow the string.
Complete the table fact.

SNAIL HOME

Fill in the missing numbers.

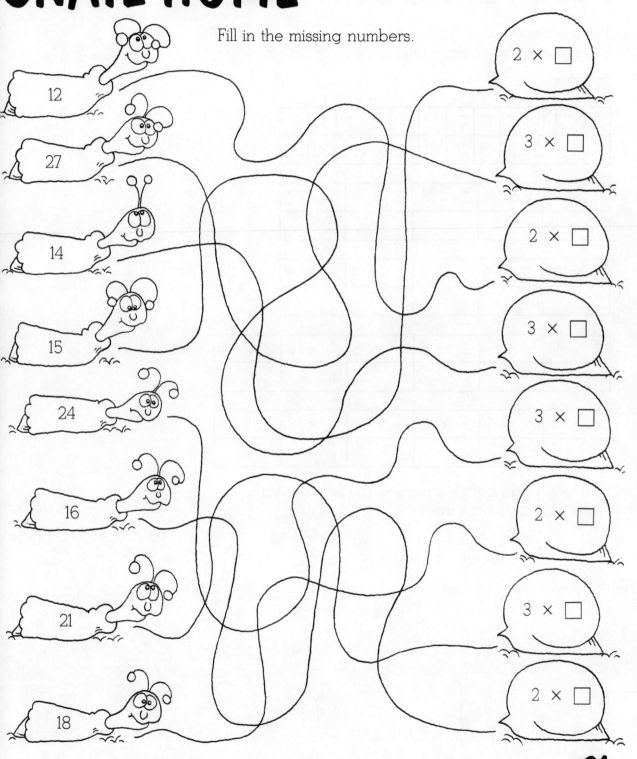

FRUIT COCKTAIL

Work out each table fact.
Use the code to change your answers to letters.

CODE											
A	C	E	G	H	L	M	N	O	P	R	Y
9	12	15	16	18	20	21	24	27	28	32	36

4 × 7	4 × 5	3 × 5	3 × 3	4 × 7
P	L	E	A	P

3 × 7	3 × 9	4 × 5	4 × 6	3 × 5
		L		E

4 × 8	3 × 5	3 × 6	4 × 8	4 × 9	3 × 4
	E				C

4 × 4	3 × 9	3 × 8	3 × 3	4 × 8	3 × 5
G			A		E

The letters can be re-arranged to spell four fruits.
Draw the fruit on the trees.

ODD-ONE-OUT

Work out the table facts.
Write the answers in words.

5 × 6
4 × 3
4 × 5

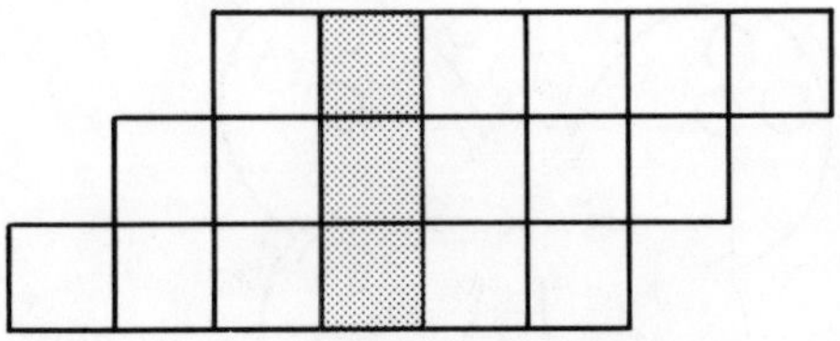

5 × 5
4 × 6
4 × 4

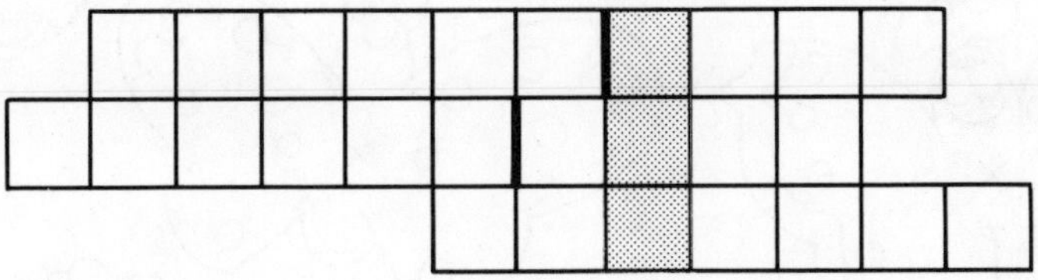

4 × 2
5 × 8
4 × 8
4 × 9
5 × 3

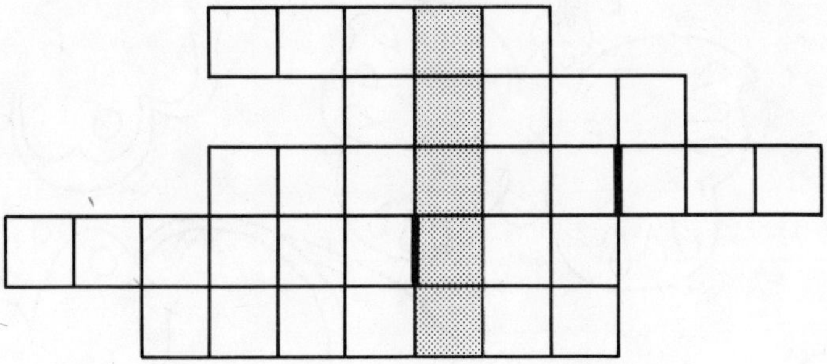

4 × 7
5 × 9
4 × 10
4 × 4
5 × 2

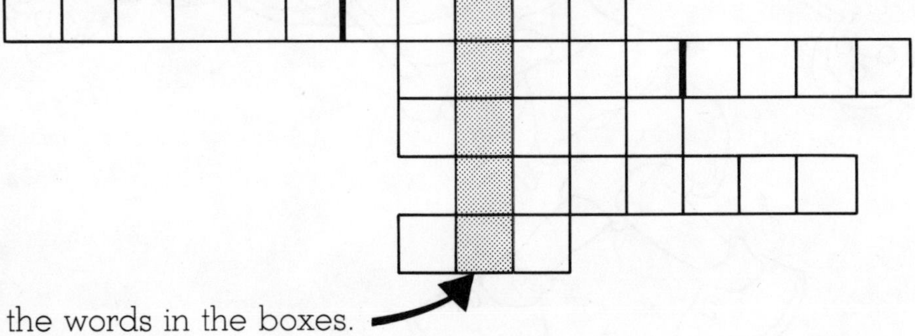

Look at the words in the boxes.
Which is the odd one out?

EVEN STEVEN

Steven only catches butterflies which have an EVEN answer.
Colour the butterflies he catches.

ELEPHANT CHAIN

Work out the table facts on the elephants.
Join the elephants up in order of size.
Begin with the smallest answer.

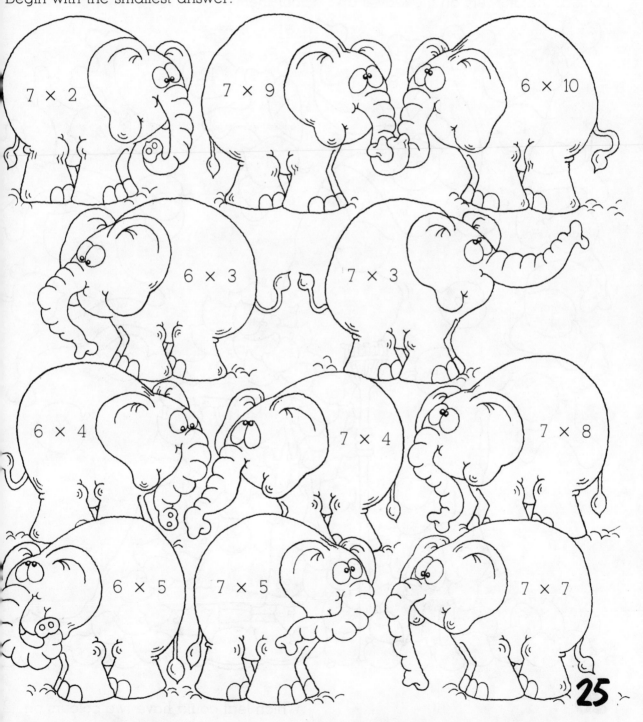

7×2

7×9

6×10

6×3

7×3

6×4

7×4

7×8

6×5

7×5

7×7

FALLING LEAVES

Leaves from the 7 × table are brown.
Leaves from the 8 × table are yellow.
Look at the answers on the leaves and colour them.

26

Which leaf could have two colours on it?

BALLOON TIES

Work out the table fact on each balloon.
Tie each balloon to its proper post.

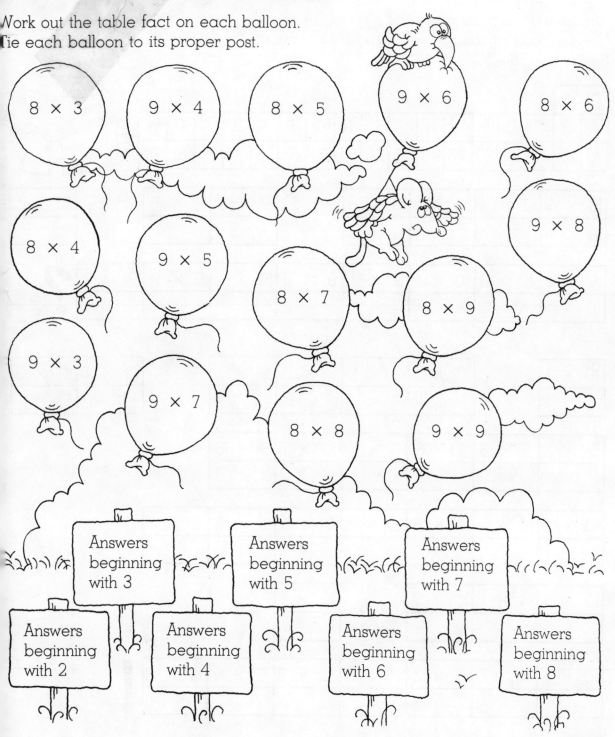

8 × 3

9 × 4

8 × 5

9 × 6

8 × 6

8 × 4

9 × 5

8 × 7

8 × 9

9 × 8

9 × 3

9 × 7

8 × 8

9 × 9

Answers beginning with 3

Answers beginning with 5

Answers beginning with 7

Answers beginning with 2

Answers beginning with 4

Answers beginning with 6

Answers beginning with 8

Which post has most balloons?

MYSTERY RIDDLE

Work out each table fact.
Use the code to change your answers into letters.
Solve the riddle.

CODE																	
A	B	C	E	F	G	H	I	L	N	O	P	R	S	T	U	W
10	18	20	27	30	36	40	45	50	54	60	63	70	72	80	81	90

10 × 9	10 × 4	10 × 1	10 × 8		9 × 5	9 × 8		10 × 1

9 × 2	10 × 1	10 × 7	9 × 2	9 × 3	10 × 2	9 × 9	9 × 3

?

10 × 1		10 × 5	9 × 5	9 × 6	9 × 3		10 × 6	10 × 3

9 × 7	9 × 3	10 × 6	9 × 7	10 × 5	9 × 3

10 × 9	10 × 1	9 × 5	10 × 8	9 × 5	9 × 6	9 × 4

10 × 3	10 × 6	10 × 7		10 × 1

10 × 4	10 × 1	9 × 5	10 × 7	10 × 2	9 × 9	10 × 8

!

28

BIRDS OF A FEATHER

Work out the table fact on each bird.
Join together birds with the same answer.

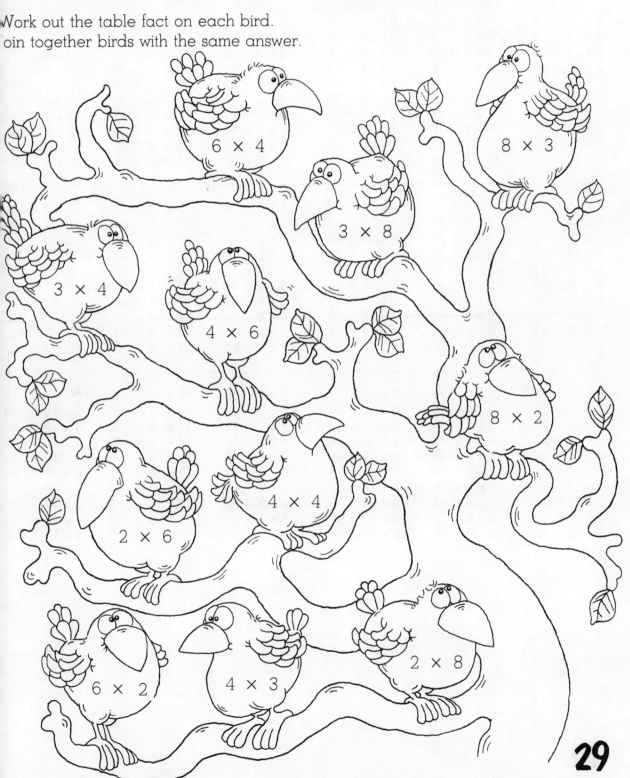

29

TABLE FACTS

2 x 1 = 2	1 x 2 = 2	3 x 1 = 3	1 x 3 = 3	4 x 1 = 4	1 x 4 = 4
2 x 2 = 4	2 x 2 = 4	3 x 2 = 6	2 x 3 = 6	4 x 2 = 8	2 x 4 = 8
2 x 3 = 6	3 x 2 = 6	3 x 3 = 9	3 x 3 = 9	4 x 3 = 12	3 x 4 = 12
2 x 4 = 8	4 x 2 = 8	3 x 4 = 12	4 x 3 = 12	4 x 4 = 16	4 x 4 = 16
2 x 5 = 10	5 x 2 = 10	3 x 5 = 15	5 x 3 = 15	4 x 5 = 20	5 x 4 = 20
2 x 6 = 12	6 x 2 = 12	3 x 6 = 18	6 x 3 = 18	4 x 6 = 24	6 x 4 = 24
2 x 7 = 14	7 x 2 = 14	3 x 7 = 21	7 x 3 = 21	4 x 7 = 28	7 x 4 = 28
2 x 8 = 16	8 x 2 = 16	3 x 8 = 24	8 x 3 = 24	4 x 8 = 32	8 x 4 = 32
2 x 9 = 18	9 x 2 = 18	3 x 9 = 27	9 x 3 = 27	4 x 9 = 36	9 x 4 = 36
2 x 10 = 20	10 x 2 = 20	3 x 10 = 30	10 x 3 = 30	4 x 10 = 40	10 x 4 = 40
5 x 1 = 5	1 x 5 = 5	6 x 1 = 6	1 x 6 = 6	7 x 1 = 7	1 x 7 = 7
5 x 2 = 10	2 x 5 = 10	6 x 2 = 12	2 x 6 = 12	7 x 2 = 14	2 x 7 = 14
5 x 3 = 15	3 x 5 = 15	6 x 3 = 18	3 x 6 = 18	7 x 3 = 21	3 x 7 = 21
5 x 4 = 20	4 x 5 = 20	6 x 4 = 24	4 x 6 = 24	7 x 4 = 28	4 x 7 = 28
5 x 5 = 25	5 x 5 = 25	6 x 5 = 30	5 x 6 = 30	7 x 5 = 35	5 x 7 = 35
5 x 6 = 30	6 x 5 = 30	6 x 6 = 36	6 x 6 = 36	7 x 6 = 42	6 x 7 = 42
5 x 7 = 35	7 x 5 = 35	6 x 7 = 42	7 x 6 = 42	7 x 7 = 49	7 x 7 = 49
5 x 8 = 40	8 x 5 = 40	6 x 8 = 48	8 x 6 = 48	7 x 8 = 56	8 x 7 = 56
5 x 9 = 45	9 x 5 = 45	6 x 9 = 54	9 x 6 = 54	7 x 9 = 63	9 x 7 = 63
5 x 10 = 50	10 x 5 = 50	6 x 10 = 60	10 x 6 = 60	7 x 10 = 70	10 x 7 = 70
8 x 1 = 8	1 x 8 = 8	9 x 1 = 9	1 x 9 = 9	10 x 1 = 10	1 x 10 = 10
8 x 2 = 16	2 x 8 = 16	9 x 2 = 18	2 x 9 = 18	10 x 2 = 20	2 x 10 = 20
8 x 3 = 24	3 x 8 = 24	9 x 3 = 27	3 x 9 = 27	10 x 3 = 30	3 x 10 = 30
8 x 4 = 32	4 x 8 = 32	9 x 4 = 36	4 x 9 = 36	10 x 4 = 40	4 x 10 = 40
8 x 5 = 40	5 x 8 = 40	9 x 5 = 45	5 x 9 = 45	10 x 5 = 50	5 x 10 = 50
8 x 6 = 48	6 x 8 = 48	9 x 6 = 54	6 x 9 = 54	10 x 6 = 60	6 x 10 = 60
8 x 7 = 56	7 x 8 = 56	9 x 7 = 63	7 x 9 = 63	10 x 7 = 70	7 x 10 = 70
8 x 8 = 64	8 x 8 = 64	9 x 8 = 72	8 x 9 = 72	10 x 8 = 80	8 x 10 = 80
8 x 9 = 72	9 x 8 = 72	9 x 9 = 81	9 x 9 = 81	10 x 9 = 90	9 x 10 = 90
8 x 10 = 80	10 x 8 = 80	9 x 10 = 90	10 x 9 = 90	10 x 10 = 100	10 x 10 = 100

ANSWERS

PAGE 3

2 × 1 = 2, 2 × 2 = 4, 2 × 3 = 6,
2 × 4 = 8, 2 × 5 = 10, 2 × 6 = 12,
2 × 7 = 14, 2 × 8 = 16, 2 × 9 = 18,
2 × 10 = 20

PAGE 5

3 × 1 = 3, 3 × 2 = 6, 3 × 3 = 9,
3 × 4 = 12, 3 × 5 = 15, 3 × 6 = 18,
3 × 7 = 21, 3 × 8 = 24, 3 × 9 = 27,
3 × 10 = 30

PAGE 6

The fish which are caught are:
3 × 6 = 18, 3 × 9 = 27, 3 × 2 = 6,
3 × 4 = 12, 3 × 8 = 24

PAGE 7

4 × 1 = 4, 4 × 2 = 8, 4 × 3 = 12,
4 × 4 = 16, 4 × 5 = 20, 4 × 6 = 24,
4 × 7 = 28, 4 × 8 = 32, 4 × 9 = 36,
4 × 10 = 40

PAGE 8

Thrush and Hawk.

PAGE 9

5 × 1 = 5, 5 × 2 = 10, 5 × 3 = 15,
5 × 4 = 20, 5 × 5 = 25, 5 × 6 = 30,
5 × 7 = 35, 5 × 8 = 40, 5 × 9 = 45,
5 × 10 = 50

PAGE 11

6 × 1 = 6, 6 × 2 = 12, 6 × 3 = 18,
6 × 4 = 24, 6 × 5 = 30, 6 × 6 = 36,
6 × 7 = 42, 6 × 8 = 48, 6 × 9 = 54,
6 × 10 = 60

PAGE 12

The number in the box is 72.
The table fact is 9 × 8 or 8 × 9.

PAGE 13

7 × 1 = 7, 7 × 2 = 14, 7 × 3 = 21,
7 × 4 = 28, 7 × 5 = 35, 7 × 6 = 42,
7 × 7 = 49, 7 × 8 = 56, 7 × 9 = 63,
7 × 10 = 70

PAGE 15

8 × 1 = 8, 8 × 2 = 16, 8 × 3 = 24,
8 × 4 = 32, 8 × 5 = 40, 8 × 6 = 48,
8 × 7 = 56, 8 × 8 = 64, 8 × 9 = 72,
8 × 10 = 80

PAGE 16

The buried bones are:
64, 40, 32, 72, 56, 16, 24, 48, 80.

PAGE 17

9 × 1 = 9, 9 × 2 = 18, 9 × 3 = 27,
9 × 4 = 36, 9 × 5 = 45, 9 × 6 = 54,
9 × 7 = 63, 9 × 8 = 72, 9 × 9 = 81,
9 × 10 = 90

PAGE 18

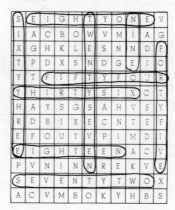

PAGE 19

10 × 1 = 10, 10 × 2 = 20, 10 × 3 = 30,
10 × 4 = 40, 10 × 5 = 50, 10 × 6 = 60,
10 × 7 = 70, 10 × 8 = 80, 10 × 9 = 90,
10 × 10 = 100

PAGE 20

A = 10 × 8, B = 10 × 4,
C = 10 × 7, D = 10 × 2,
E = 10 × 9, F = 10 × 6

PAGE 21

12 = 2 × 6, 27 = 3 × 9, 14 = 2 × 7,
15 = 3 × 5, 24 = 3 × 8, 16 = 2 × 8,
21 = 3 × 7, 18 = 2 × 9

PAGE 22

APPLE, LEMON, CHERRY, ORANGE

PAGE 23

HEN, FOX, HORSE, GOOSE
The fox is the odd one out. All the others are found
in the farmyard.

PAGE 24

The butterflies Steven catches are:
6 × 2, 6 × 6, 6 × 8, 6 × 9, 6 × 7,
5 × 4, 6 × 5.

PAGE 25

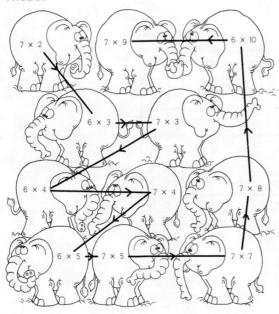

PAGE 26

The leaf with two colours is 56.

PAGE 27

The post with most balloons is 4. (3 balloons)

PAGE 28

What is a barbecue?
A line of people wating for a haircut.

PAGE 29

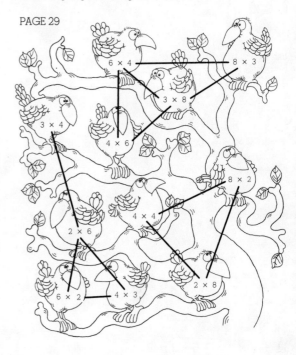